Merry Christmas from Santa Claus

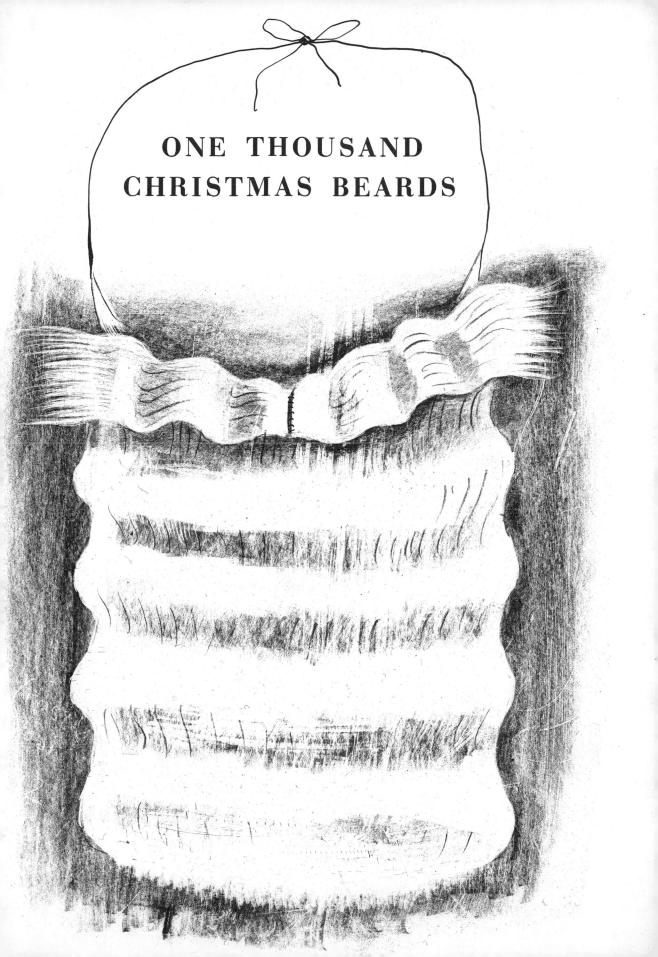

ONE THOUSAND
CHRISTMAS BEARDS

ALFRED · A · KNOPF NEW YORK

ONE THOUSAND
CHRISTMAS BEARDS

by Roger Duvoisin

At Christmas time,
when snowflakes fly all about,
when windows are hung with Christmas wreaths,
and fir trees are bright with lights,
all the Santa Clauses come out into the streets.

All the Santa Clauses?
Are there many Santas?
Or is there only one?

If you wish to know,
open the door of Santa's igloo,
(only a little, not enough to let the cold come in)
and listen:

"Am I angry!" Santa was saying to Mrs. Santa.
"One hundred, one thousand times angry
to see, when Christmas comes,
so many people with red suits like mine,
and false beards and wigs
that make them resemble me.
Wherever I go, I meet Santas—
Santa Clauses everywhere!
Some are fat and some are thin,
some are tall and some are small,
some have red noses like circus clowns,
some are shabby and some are neat.
By my own real beard,
I'll put an end to those false Santas!
There is only *one* Santa Claus,
and *that's me!*"

"Do not excite yourself," said Mrs. Santa.
"You will get hot and then catch cold.
Soon you will forget all about it."

It was true that Santa
could not be angry very long.
The next day he worked at his toys
as gaily and happily as ever.

But the following Christmas,
when he went on his rounds
and saw Santas all about town,
he got angry all over again.
With his face as red as his suit,

he declared war on the false Santas.
He hunted them in the streets—
in the stores—in the subways.
Wherever he found them, he sprang upon them
and snatched their false beards away.

There was the doorman Santa,
who helped people out of taxi cabs;
he was a Santa as big as a bear
with a pillow for a stomach.

Santa snatched his beard and wig with a jerk
and put them into his bag.

There was the sandwich man Santa,
who was so thin
his red suit hung on him

like a flag on a pole on a windless day.
Santa got his beard
with a shout of victory.

There was the farmer Santa,
who sold Christmas trees
and beat his feet on the sidewalk
to keep warm.

He had a false red nose
above his false beard.
They were both put away
into Santa's bag.

There was the trumpeter Santa,
who stood at the curb
and played on his trumpet.
He played a screeching false note
when Santa took his beard away.

There was the merchant Santa,
who carried dolls on a tray
and cried along the street:
"Dolls for sale! A quarter for a doll!"
The doll in his hand said, "Mama!"
when Santa pulled off this Santa's beard.

There was the shabby Santa,
who had finished his day's work
and waited for the subway
to take him home.

There was also the Santa
who sang *Silent Night* by a false chimney,
and sounded a bell
to call passersby to drop their coins.

There was the wax Santa,
who smiled day and night
amidst the hats
of the hat store window.

And the salesman Santa,
who sat in a store
to draw customers
to his display of Christmas cards.

There was the tired Santa,
who sat in a cafeteria
with his cup of hot coffee.

This one did not wait for Santa
to snatch his beard.
"Here, take it," he said.
"I can't drink my coffee with it on."

There were more, many more false Santas!
When Santa had pulled all their false beards,
and frightened them all into hiding,
he was ready to ride back home.

Great was Santa's pride
when he called Mrs. Santa out
to show her his trophies:
a sleighful of Christmas beards!

Alas, his pride melted away
like a snowman in the sun
when she looked at him
and said severely:
"Santa, you cruel man,
did you kill all the false Santas
who wore those false beards?"

"No, I didn't," said Santa,
"but I put an end
to their trying to look like me."

"Santa, you are so silly!
You never stopped to think, did you,
why there are lots of Santas about
when Christmas comes.
In how many places can you be at one time?"

"Why, *one*, of course."

"Then, how do you think people can have
true Christmas cheer in their towns
when they see you for only a moment
or not at all?"

"They can't very well, can they?"

"Yes, they can. That's why so many dress like you;
it makes the streets and the stores more cheerful.
Children like to look at you so much!
They would have a sad Christmas indeed
with no Santa about."

Good Santa was now very sorry
about all those beards in his sleigh.
He wrapped them up into as many packages
and mailed them all back to their owners.
He even included a box of candy with each beard.

Thereafter, the more Santas
he saw at Christmas time,
the happier he was!

Merry Christmas
from
Roger Duvoisin